Organising Idea No. 5

*A monograph published for the*
EUROPEAN THERAPY STUDIES INSTITUTE

The Shackled Brain

How to release locked-in patterns of trauma



H G Publishing for the
European Therapy Studies Institute
Chalvington, Hailsham, East Sussex BN27 3TD, United Kingdom

Printed in Great Britain

ISBN 1 899398 11 2

# The Shackled Brain

## How to release locked-in patterns of trauma

Joseph Griffin and Ivan Tyrrell

"While fear is a part of everyone's life, too much
or inappropriate fear accounts
for many common psychiatric problems."

*Joseph LeDoux*

"Who would believe that so small a space could contain
the images of the whole universe?"

*Leonardo da Vinci*

## Organising Ideas

"All scientific knowledge is a correlation of *what* is seen with the *way* that it is seen."

Henri Bortoft, *The Wholeness of Nature*

In all fields confusion flourishes, mistakes are made and harm is done when we forget that the *way* we look at phenomena is dependent on an active effort of imagination and thinking. We are not mechanical recording instruments looking out on a fixed world (although this is certainly the philosophy of science which is usually communicated by the way science is taught in schools, presented in popular books and revealed in television programmes). We *organise* what we see through what we believe we know.

When a field of study is confused about something, it usually needs a new organising idea.

An organising idea plays an active role in shaping our perception, thinking and research and is always larger than earlier ideas because it has to explain the anomalies that previously caused confusion.

This paper, one of a series commissioned by the European Therapy Studies Institute, offers a new organising idea.

*ETSI 2001*

"And you pick whatever lock is presented to you. And once one lock is unpicked, all the other locks become vulnerable."

*Milton H. Erickson*

# The Shackled Brain

## How to release locked-in patterns of trauma

A TRAUMATISED creature lives a private hell: hyperalert, terrorised by an invisible mental wound, helplessly in thrall to a powerful emotional memory of a life-threatening event – or series of events – real or imagined. Horrific, violent events can clearly impact on the mind as well as the body to produce such a state, as vividly illustrated in the following description of a Vietnam war veteran's experience:

"I can't get the memories out of my mind! The images come flooding back in vivid detail, triggered by the most inconsequential things, like a door slamming or the smell of stir-fried pork. Last night I went to bed, was having a good sleep for a change. Then ... there was a bolt of crackling thunder. I awoke instantly, frozen in fear. I am right back in Vietnam. My hands are freezing, yet sweat pours from my entire body. I feel each hair on the back of my neck standing on end. I can't catch my breath and my heart is pounding ... The next clap of thunder makes me jump so much that I fall to the floor."[1]

Although originally post traumatic stress disorder (PTSD) was most commonly diagnosed among soldiers, sailors and airmen returning from war zones, current American estimates are that at least eight per cent of the general population ultimately develop it as a result of traumatic experiences, ranging from surviving terrifying natural disasters such as earthquakes, forest fires or avalanches, to car, rail, boat or air accidents, heart attacks, mugging, burning, rape or sexual assault.[2]

We now also realise that people can be vicariously traumatised. Some grandchildren of concentration camp survivors, for example, have subsequently become traumatised by hearing about their grandparents' memories.[3] A female client of one of us (JG), whose son and fiancée were horribly burnt to death in a tragic car accident, suffered terrifying traumatic flashbacks from her imagined fantasies about what it must have been like to be trapped in a car burning to death like that.

It is clear, however, from any review of the literature, that, though there is now widespread agreement as to what constitutes PTSD (see Appendix I), there is still tremendous confusion among clinicians about how best to help people who suffer from it.[4] Indeed, critical incident debriefing, the most widely available approach, in which people are usually asked to relive in great detail their terrible experiences, has often been found to make the condition worse. The very people whom this technique is designed to help, namely those who are at risk of developing PTSD, are in fact those most likely to be harmed by the process.[5,6,7,8]

Other treatments on offer include pharmacological, behavioural, psychodynamic and cognitive methods, hypnotic techniques including EMDR (eye-movement desensitisation and reprocessing – see Appendix III), and various versions of exposure therapy, such as flooding or systematic desensitisation. Many of these approaches may work in the short or long term, but the sheer variety of them, together with the lack of reliability of effect, indicates a failure to understand the psychobiology of traumatic stress reactions. (This is a reflection of a wider problem in psychotherapy and counselling, which still largely operates out of prescientific models and has yet to incorporate recent discoveries about brain functioning into many commonly practised procedures.[9])

## The brain and the P in APET

We believe that, drawing on the APET model[10] which has been developed to incorporate recent bioneurological discoveries, we can offer a new understanding of PTSD and show why some treatments are more effective than others.

The four letters, APET, represent an easy way to remember the specific processes through which the mind/body system works. The **A** stands for an activating agent: a stimulus from the environment. The **P** symbolises the pattern-matching processes of the mind, which in turn give rise to emotion, **E**, which can produce **T**, thoughts.

In PTSD the activating agent, the **A**, is the event that a person has experienced or witnessed which involved actual or threatened serious physical harm to them.

Pattern matching, the **P** in APET, is the process by which the brain habitually organises experience and makes sense of it. It works in the following way.

During the rapid eye movement (REM) sleep of neonates and newborns, nature lays down the programmes, or templates, for instinctive behaviours.[11] These templates are necessarily not highly specific, so as to allow us to react flexibly as we grow and interact with the world.[12] All human babies respond, for example, to 'face-like' shapes rather than to any one precisely defined face, and start to look for a face to communicate with from the moment they calm down after being born.[13] In other words, the patterns given to us are only *partially* specified by nature. Throughout our lives our brains are constantly seeking to match up these given templates to suitable stimuli in the environment. But it is never a perfect match, only a part match.[14]

Pattern matching is also the process by which the brain's alarm system, an organ in the limbic system called the amygdala, seeks to ensure an organism's survival. It constantly scans the environment for potential threats, comparing all incoming stimulation supplied by our various senses with survival templates – fear memories – to see if they are life threatening or life enhancing. A crackle of twigs or a sudden silence in the forest may trigger the alarm system because previous experience of a crackle or silence has signalled a predator, setting in train an emotional reaction which leads to freezing, fight or flight. The experience is formed into a sensory memory and is passed on to an adjacent organ in the brain called the hippocampus. Here all of our most recent experiences are stored before they are transferred to the neocortex and translated into narrative memory.

When a deeply traumatic event occurs, however, the emotional reaction is so strong that communication between the amygdala and the hippocampus is barred, preventing the sensory memories from passing from the one to the other and keeping them trapped in wordless form in the amygdala.[*, 15] This is when PTSD ensues.

About 25 per cent of people exposed to traumatic events develop PTSD, according to American research.[16] Susceptibility depends upon a variety of factors such as the degree of trauma and personality factors, such as trait anxiety and suggestibility.[17] The amygdala of a person exposed to a life-threatening traumatic event who does go on to develop PTSD has literally been imprinted with the pattern of the trauma which contains all the information surrounding the event.[18] Thereafter the templates contained in the amygdala, and to which all new incoming stimuli are compared, also include a template for that traumatic event. Whenever there is a match, *or a part-match,* the amygdala fires off the alarm reaction, the fight or flight reflex is activated and, because this all happens at an

---

* It has to be said that the precise way in which the amygdala, hippocampus and other parts of the brain interact and create and store memories is not yet completely clear.

unconscious level, the person experiences an incomprehensible state of alarm.

It is because the pattern matching is a metaphorical process – the amygdala is looking for something *like* something else – that people experience flashbacks and other severe alarm reactions when the amygdala spots anything that has an approximate similarity to some aspect of a traumatic event. This is why the origin of such reactions can at first seem mysterious. A graphic example of this is provided by the tale of a butcher in the 1920s who began to have 'strange spells': his heart would beat violently, he would vomit and then lose consciousness. It emerged that these attacks usually followed exposure to certain odours from volatile oils – perfume, lemon oil, banana oil, or ether. The butcher's shop he worked in was frequented by fashionable women, many of whom came heavily perfumed, and, as his doctor described it, "when they would enter the butcher shop ... the patient would become dizzy and lose consciousness". It turned out that, during the Great War of 1914–18, the butcher had had the horribly unpleasant experience of being gassed in the trenches while asleep. "The flushing, the rapid pulse, the dizziness and the vomiting," his doctor decided, were "a repetition of the original traumatic event which overtook him in sleep." The man's amygdala was simply pattern matching to *any* strange, strong smell.[19]

In the same way, people who have survived horrific car accidents can have exaggerated alarm reactions to the mere sight of a car, the smell of petrol, or even just the sound of screeching brakes on a television programme. People who have experienced a violent, traumatising sexual attack can later, in a loving relationship, become highly anxious at any form of sexual approach and withdraw from normal sexual intimacy.

We can now see that critical incident debriefing puts a traumatised victim and their counsellor into a double-bind situation. To use Daniel Goleman's memorable term from his book *Emotional Intelligence*,[20] emotional arousal "hijacks" the thinking part of the brain. The more emotionally aroused we are, the less able we are to think straight – as anyone who has ever fallen in love or lost their temper will know. If the counsellor invites the victim to talk about or recall the trauma, hoping to help them set it in context and put it behind them, an emotional charge is set off which inhibits the higher neocortex from functioning. Without input from the neocortex, there is no feedback mechanism available to the brain to detraumatise the memory. Each time an attempt is made to recall the trauma, off goes the alarm, the higher neocortex is inhibited and the traumatic memory is further programmed into the amygdala, thus deepening the trauma in the person's emotional brain.

Sad to say, this is the effect of most counselling for trauma as practised in this country. When counsellors encourage traumatised clients to recreate their memories of the trauma, they embed the trauma even more strongly.

## Fight, flight or freeze

We would like to put forward an explanation for why some people are especially susceptible to PTSD. When we are exposed to a sudden and significant stress that we feel may endanger our life, our attention is intensely and instantly fully focused on the source of the threat. Momentarily we freeze, stuck to the ground like mesmerised rabbits. Then, in most people, the fight or flight response is activated. We defend ourselves or run away. But some individuals stay in the freeze response, paralysed, dumb and insensitive to stimuli. This may be especially likely to happen if an escape route is blocked.[21]

In evolutionary terms, freezing was – and is – actually beneficial for many animals. If you suddenly stop moving you become invisible to those predators whose main focus is on movement and so have a better chance of staying alive.[22] Naturalists watching animals being hunted have noticed that the freezing response occurs an instant *before* the predator makes physical contact with its intended prey. Peter Levine, an international expert on trauma and stress, and holder of a doctorate in medical and biological physics, has vividly described what happens as a cheetah closes in on an impala. "It is almost as if the animal has surrendered to its impending demise. But the fallen impala is not dead. Although on the 'outside' it appears limp and motionless, on the 'inside' its nervous system is still activated from the 70 miles an hour chase. Though barely breathing, the impala's heart is pumping at extreme rates. Its brain and body are being flooded by the same chemicals (for example, adrenaline and cortisol) that helped fuel its attempted escape.

"It is possible that the impala will not be devoured immediately. The mother cheetah may drag its fallen, apparently dead, prey behind a bush and seek out its cubs who are hiding at a safe distance. Herein lies a short window of opportunity for the impala.

"The temporarily 'frozen' creature has a chance to awaken from its state of shock, shake and tremble in order to discharge the vast amount of energy stored in its nervous system, then, as if nothing had happened, bound away in search of the rest of its herd.

"Another benefit of the frozen (immobility) state is its analgesic nature. If the impala *is* killed, it will be spared the pain of its own demise."[23]

Though it appears that we have separated ourselves from animals like the impala and cheetah, our responses to threat are still biologically formed. They are human givens – innate and instinctive functions of our organism. For the impala, life-threatening situations are an everyday occurrence, so it makes sense that the ability to resolve and complete these episodes is built into their biological systems. Threat, albeit of a different kind, is a relatively common phenomenon for humans as well. Though we are rarely aware of it, we also possess the innate ability to complete and resolve these experiences. From our biology come our responses to threat, and it is also in our biology that the resolution of trauma dwells.

In order to remain healthy, all animals, including humans, must discharge the vast energies mobilised for survival. This discharge completes our activated responses to threat, and allows us to return to a more normal state. In biology, this process is called homoeostasis: the ability of an organism to respond appropriately to any given circumstance, and then return to a baseline of what could be called 'normal' functioning.

In the National Geographic video *Polar Bear Alert*, a frightened bear is seen being run down by a pursuing aeroplane, shot with a tranquilliser dart, surrounded by wildlife biologists, and then tagged. Later, as the massive animal comes out of its state of shock, it begins to quiver, and ends up in almost convulsive shaking – its limbs flailing around seemingly out of control. The shaking subsides and the animal is seen to take three long spontaneous breaths which seem to spread through its entire body.

The biologist narrating the film comments that what the bear is doing is shaking off the stress accumulated during its capture. It is pointed out that, if the sequence is looked at again but slowed down in speed, it suddenly becomes clear that the seemingly uncontrolled leg movements are in effect coordinated running movements. The animal seems to be completing its 'flight' template, cut short when it was trapped, discharging frozen energy.[24]

Animals and most humans *don't* get traumatised when they can properly discharge their accumulated stress energy by activating the fight or flight reflex at the time of the event. So, what is happening in those who *do* develop PTSD and are, therefore, holding a long term effect in their psychobiology?

There is another everyday state in which mammals, including humans, become paralysed or frozen. It is during the rapid eye movement (REM) state, the deep trance state we all slip into when we are asleep and dreaming. When we dream, the very same 'orientation response' (the reaction which turns our attention to a sudden unexpected stimulus, such as a loud noise, and freezes our behaviour when awake) fires off while we are sleeping.[25] It has the same basic function because dreaming is nature's design for defusing emotional arousal patterns from the day that have not been discharged, and the orientation response alerts the brain to these. Discharge is achieved in a dream, through a metaphorical representation of the incomplete arousal pattern. The dream thus deactivates the emotional stress.[26]

The freezing or paralysis of movement which is triggered by the orientation response also occurs in the dream state (and prevents us from acting our dreams out).

As mentioned earlier, it is during the REM state that the foetal and neonatal brain is programmed with all its instinctive templates. The state of hypnosis is a trance state with many features of similarity to that of the REM state, often including paralysis, and it is when an individual is in this deeply relaxed state that new learning can best be programmed. All forms of hypnotic induction work by duplicating part of the REM state programming: for example triggering rapid eye movements can induce a hypnotic state, so can firing the orientation response through shock, or relaxation (which triggers off the pathways to body paralysis in the REM state). Hypnotic inductions are artificial ways of consciously accessing the REM state.[27] This is why hypnosis is such a powerful psychological tool for raising self esteem, increasing confidence or helping an individual practise new skills or improve their social performance. Hypnosis, then, is the trance state which makes us most receptive to new learning or programming, whether for good or ill, just as the REM state is in the young.

Similarly, we suggest, in the paralysis of the freeze state during trauma, the amygdala is programmed to retain fear. People who have been 'paralysed' by fear and who develop post traumatic stress disorder have been in a profound trance during the trauma, during which the horrific experience is deeply etched into the amygdala, where the survival templates are stored. From then on, whenever the amygdala finds a match or part-match for that experience in the environment, even just a thought or memory, it sets off the alarm reaction.

We would therefore expect to find that the people most prone to PTSD are those who are also most highly hypnotisable. And this has been shown to be so.[28]

When people have been badly frightened, talking about what happened can be a way of integrating the event and converting it into a normal memory. In such cases, 'talking it out' can be helpful. But for those people at highest risk of developing PTSD, any counselling or critical incident debriefing that gets them in touch with their emotions will, like a post hypnotic suggestion, cue them to relive the trauma, trigger off the emotional reaction, and further embed it in.

## Creating calm

Effective treatment, by contrast, will involve removing the traumatic sensory memory from the amygdala, where it is stored, and incorporating it into normal functioning memory in the higher cortex. To do this, the more objective intelligence of the neocortex must be helped to evaluate the imprint, see that it no longer represents a threat in the here and now, and modify it. Once the information is processed in this way it becomes a normal working memory. It will remain an unpleasant one, but part of normal functioning; not something shadowy that keeps the brain continually on the alert while scanning the environment for danger, and thereby maintaining the person in a state of high arousal.

Furthermore, when the trauma template is released, attention capacity is freed up. People literally become more intelligent again because the data-processing capability of the brain is no longer devoted to holding that trauma template in place.

The history of 20th century military psychiatry is full of examples of doctors and psychiatrists struggling to find ways to help traumatised individuals (the 'shell-shocked' as they were first called) and discover why some individuals seemed more prone to 'crack' under extreme pressure than others.[29] Some had great success, particularly those using hypnosis. This was a common treatment during the First World War when it was widely observed that 'hysterics' were highly hypnotisable and open to suggestion (shown by the ease with which they copied one another's symptoms).[30] The following is a description of such work by Dr William Brown, a mathematician and philosopher who took up academic psychology and graduated in medicine. At the outbreak of war he was reader in psychology at London University and a well-known academic expert on hypnosis. He gained practical experience with trauma victims in shell-shock hospitals in England and then went to work at front-line hospitals in France because he believed early treatment was important. About 15 per cent of the cases he dealt with concerned what we would call severe trauma symptoms and PTSD and for these he used hypnosis:

"The patient would be brought into hospital lying on a stretcher, perhaps dumb, trembling violently, perspiring profusely, his face showing an expression of great terror, his eyes either with a fixed stare or rolling from side to side. When one questioned him and got him to answer in writing he would tell one that he was unable to remember what had happened to him. In some way or other he had been knocked out and had come to to find that he was paralysed and unable to speak.

"I interview him alone in my office and tell him in a tone of conviction that I shall restore his speech to him in a few seconds if he will do exactly what I say. I then urge him to lie down upon a couch, close his eyes and think of sleep. I urge him to give himself up to sleep, to let sleep come to him, as it assuredly will. I tell him that he is getting drowsy, his limbs are getting heavy with sleep, all his muscles are relaxed, he is breathing more and more slowly, more and more deeply. Above all, that his eyelids are getting heavy, as heavy as lead, that he feels disinclined to open them however hard he tries. At this stage, which generally supervenes within two or three minutes, he really cannot open his eyes. This is a stage of very light hypnosis quite sufficient for my purposes.

"I now tell him that the moment I put my hand on his forehead he will seem to be back again in the trenches, in the firing line, in the fighting, as the case may be, and will live again through the experiences he had when the shock occurred. This I say in a tone of absolute conviction, as if there is not the slightest shadow of possibility of my words not coming true. I then place my hand on his forehead. He immediately begins to twist and turn on the couch and shouts out in a terror-stricken voice. He talks as he talked at the time when he received the shock. He really does live again through the experiences of that awful time. Sometimes he speaks as if in dialogue, punctuated with intervals of silence corresponding to the remarks of his interlocutor, like a person speaking at the telephone. At other times he indulges in imprecations [cursing and pleading] and soliloquy. In some cases he is able to reply to my questions and give an account of his experiences. In others he cannot do so, but continues to writhe and talk as if he were still in the throes of the actual experience. In every case he speaks and acts as if he were again under the influence of the terrifying emotion. It is as if this emotion had been originally repressed, and the power of speech with it, and is now being worked off and worked out."[31]

After such sessions the patients would collapse into a profound sleep.

British psychiatrist Dr William Sargant described working with traumatised soldiers during the Second World War. His treatment, like many doctors before him, was to encourage an emotional abreaction because it was often found that sufferers aroused to extremes of terror by hypnosis, drama or drugs would collapse and, on waking, be fully recovered. In 1944 he began using ether to induce abreaction with traumatised soldiers because "ether released a far greater degree of explosive excitement, which made their recital of events extremely poignant or dramatic". Furthermore, "the sudden states of collapse, after emotional outbursts induced by ether, were far more frequent than after those induced by hypnosis or barbiturates".

"Under ether, certain patients could easily be persuaded to relive experiences of terror, anger, or other excitement. Some of them might then collapse from emotional exhaustion and lie motionless for a minute or so, unmoved by ordinary stimuli; and, on coming round, would often burst into a flood of tears and report that their outstanding symptoms had suddenly disappeared. Or they would describe their minds as now freed of the terror aroused by certain obsessive pictures; they could still think of these, if they wished, but without the former hysterical anxiety. When simple excitement at the recital of past experiences did not reach the phase of ... collapse, little or no change or mental improvement might be observed in the patient; if, however, the abreactive treatment was repeated, and drugs were used to increase the amount of emotional stimulation until collapse supervened, sudden improvement could occur."[32]

Sargant also found that, if he couldn't get a description of the traumatic event from his patients, he could invent horrific stories, of soldiers trapped in burning tanks for example, tell them to his patients and this would be sufficient to induce the necessary fear arousal prior to the abreactive collapse. In other words, by pattern matching to *any* terrifying aspect of an event – loud noises, fire, feelings of helplessness etc. – the amygdala's alarm response would fire. As we would expect, an exact match was not required. The importance of this part of Sargant's work is that it showed that even if the surface details of a pattern or a template were different, as long as it was a frightening situation associated with war, it would trigger a state of terror. And, if this crude pattern match was deactivated, the work was done.

Having earlier said that the emotional arousal created during most types of critical incident debriefing can cause harm to those at risk of PTSD, we now appear to be saying that, sometimes, getting people really worked up and emotionally aroused appears to help them to recover. The two statements are not, in fact, at odds. An erroneous tendency has been to assume that it is the emotional arousal itself that heals the person. But the real active ingredient, as Sargant observed, is the collapse into a totally calm state after exposure to the emotionally arousing stimuli (even if the stimuli are in an individual's imagination). The memory can then be transferred through to, and processed in, the higher cortex. The active ingredient for effective therapy is *calmness*.

The reason, for instance, that exposure therapy can and very often does work for severe phobic reactions is because the aim is for a person to stay in a recreated fear situation until the emotional arousal (usually a terror of dying as a result of exposure to the feared object or circumstance) subsides and calmness follows. Once the person is calm, the neocortex is released from its emotional shackles and is free to evaluate what has occurred. Having clear evidence that the fear is unwarranted (death didn't ensue), the brain can successfully reprocess its understanding of the stimulus.

It is only if the person stays in the situation *until the emotional arousal goes down,* however, that exposure therapy works. The danger with exposure therapy is that, if the person cannot handle the highly unpleasant arousal and leaves the situation before they are calm, the trauma will have been programmed in even deeper. This is the problem too with most types of critical incident debriefing. Emotional reliving of the trauma is encouraged and is sufficient to create an emotional charge but not generally to achieve collapse and calm.

Clearly, it is highly painful to re-experience trauma to the point of collapse. The value of the fast phobia technique, shortly to be described, is that such terrifying emotional arousal can be bypassed completely and the desired calm state be created at the outset. It is, therefore, a faster process, much less dangerous and much, much less unpleasant.

## The observing self

In trance states induced by emotional arousal, an individual's attention is locked into a particular way of looking at reality. We are stuck in a one-sided view when we are fiercely angry, besotted by love or overly anxious. In other words, emotional arousal takes away our ability to see the full picture. The converse is a state of awareness which has been termed the 'observing self' by American psychiatrist Arthur Deikman.[33] (See also Appendix V.)

The observing self is a state of pure awareness where we have the potential to look in many directions and can *choose* to focus our attention in a variety of ways. At a biological level this occurs when the organism relaxes and the neocortex can function without excessive emotional interference, enabling us to look at reality more objectively. The objective 'take' on reality, which is the province of the neocortex, counterbalances the emotional 'take' of the limbic system, which is always based upon the past and is much more subjective.

While it is useful to be able to draw upon the past, we also need to be able to question whether the past is relevant to whatever it is that we are doing here and now. That is the role of the observing self. It enables us to delay and impact upon emotional responses by its ability to evaluate a situation. It asks, in effect: "Look, is this the appropriate way to go? What other possibilities are there? What might be the consequences if I take a certain course of action?"[34]

When we keep calm and engage the observing self we can take a different view of a traumatic memory and say, "Yes, that was a dangerous moment at that time, but that was then – in the past – which is not now," thereby giving the feedback to the limbic system that a fear pattern of response is no longer relevant. When a traumatised person has been helped to step back into their observing self and view the situation dispassionately they are cured. The traumatic memory becomes an ordinary memory.

A person must be in a state of low arousal to engage the observing self because communication lines from the neocortex to the emotional brain are much more restricted than communication from the emotional brain to the neocortex.[35] We need to be in that relaxed state of 'no mind' for the feedback mechanism to work.

Helping clients back into their observing self, and refocusing their attention so that their neocortex can engage with problems, is a fundamental step in counselling for all forms of anxiety and emotional disorders. Once a client's attention mechanism is opened up so that they can see the bigger picture, they are inevitably provided with a healthier way of looking at their situation and seeing where and how the need to change comes into it. So, for example, somebody suffering from depression due to negatively introspecting about having Parkinson's disease, needs to be told, directly and indirectly, that *they and Parkinson's disease are not one and the same.* With some people, one can occasionally effect a dramatic recovery simply by making that distinction very clear to them: saying, for example, "*You* are *not* your cancer," to someone depressed about their illness. (A good example of a therapist successfully doing this, and saving a young anorexic's life, is given in the Organising Ideas Monograph No. 2, see page 57.) However, this may need to be done over and over again in different ways until the penny drops. People are not their disease, their feelings or their behaviour: diseases, destructive feelings and inappropriate behaviours are problems on to which we all have to bring our problem-solving capacities to bear. No one is a *fundamentally* damaged or dysfunctional human being while they can still do this. It is via the observing self that all hope is found.

## How to cure post traumatic stress disorder

With the understanding of *why* people can suffer long-term traumatisation – the imprint of a life-threatening event is embedded in the amygdala which continually scans the environment, pattern matching to anything similar to elements of that event – we can solve the problem of *how* to remove the imprint and 'convince' the amygdala that the imprinted template is no longer necessary for survival. One of the little acknowledged breakthroughs in psychotherapy in recent times has been the development of an effective and relatively painless way of doing just that.

The technique, now commonly called the fast phobia cure, evolved out of the technique promoted by Richard Bandler, one of the co-founders of Neurolinguistic Programming (NLP). He, in turn, was inspired by observing the renowned psychiatrist and hypnotherapist Milton H. Erickson detraumatise people. The method is variously known as the fast phobia cure (because it is most often used by hypnotherapists for curing phobias), the 'rewind technique' (which is the name preferred by clinical psychologists) and, by those who practise NLP, the V/K dissociation technique (the V stands for visual and the K for kinaesthetic – feelings).

The version of the technique which is recommended by the European Therapy Studies Institute (ETSI) has been refined and streamlined to make it easier to teach and carry out. Clinical experience shows that it works reliably with almost all cases of post traumatic stress disorder and phobia, but up till now there has been no satisfactory published explanation for why it works.

This trauma resolution method is not difficult to learn to do, provided the practitioner has the aptitude and sufficient spare capacity to devote concentrated attention to the traumatised individual they are working with. Many medical and psychiatric professionals have attended one-day training workshops run by MindFields College to learn the technique and have subsequently been able to help even the most severely traumatised people.[36] Obviously, the more practice one has in using the technique with real cases, the more skilled one becomes.

What this technique achieves, when employed by a competent practitioner, is the taking of a traumatic memory and turning it into an ordinary memory. This is done by bringing the client's observing self into play while keeping them at a low level of arousal. By removing traumatic memories in the way we recommend, the observing self is enabled to view the troubling pattern of memory and, using the neural connections between the limbic system, where the trauma is 'trapped' or 'imprinted', and the neocortex, reframe it as no longer an active threat to the person.

This is an artificial way of doing what nature does with all learning (another process that is a human given). All of us have memories of events that were emotionally arousing or even life threatening at the time, which we can now look back on and tell an amusing anecdote about. Those memories have moved out of the amygdala's traumatic store, so to speak, into ordinary functioning memory.

Any mechanism that enables a traumatic memory to be turned into an ordinary memory is going to cure phobias and post traumatic stress. But the human givens approach uses the most direct path: keeping the physiological arousal level down so that the neocortex of the observing self can set up the feedback loops necessary to reframe that memory.

When properly applied, the technique will cure phobias, even serious ones, in one session. It is also an excellent way to detraumatise disturbing flashbacks and post traumatic stress symptoms arising from any kind of event perceived as life threatening. But for people who have a history of abuse the technique may need to be used over a period of time to deal separately with all the major incidents that the person is still traumatised by.

## The therapeutic procedure

The first step is very simple: lowering the arousal level prior to the memory being recalled. The client is induced to become calm, comfortable and relaxed whilst imagining they are in a special place – a beautiful garden, a beach, or in some other natural environment of their choosing where they feel safe. Guided imagery, or visualisation (in other words, basic hypnotic skills) is necessary for this, though it doesn't matter what terminology you use. Many people are uncomfortable with the word hypnosis, and the aim is purely to get the client relaxed enough to slip into the REM trance state.

The second step is to get the client to begin recalling the memory in a dissociated state *whilst remaining calm.* Dissociation separates the observing self from the emotional self. A first position dissociation can be achieved by asking clients to imagine watching themselves doing something. Imagining watching oneself watching oneself doing something (for example watching oneself watching oneself on TV) is called a second position dissociation. The resultant increased separation between the observing self and the arousing event makes the feelings associated with it much less intense. If the process sounds complex, it is, in fact, easy in practice.

We get clients to imagine that they are watching a portable television set (portable because clients can be extraordinarily concrete in their thinking whilst in trance, and demand to know where they can plug the set in, if they are out in the open!). To ensure that they are comfortable with the visualisation process, we might then ask them to use the remote control button to bring up on the screen an image of themselves, such as a happy holiday photograph. This is a first position dissociation because they are looking at themselves on the screen. The second step is to ask clients to imagine floating out of their bodies to one side and watch themselves looking at an image of themselves on the screen – second position dissociation.

Now the trauma can be replayed on the screen in fast forward mode without setting off an emotional charge in the client. This is because the client isn't looking directly at the trauma, but at a representation of themselves watching the trauma being replayed on the television screen. We ask them to play the incident through from a point before anything frightening had happened to a point after the trauma was over, when they knew that they were safe. If a client had been mugged, for example, this point might be when they have got home and know that they are safe indoors. If the client has been involved in a car accident, they might be observing themselves safe in hospital.

By having the client operate a remote control device in their imagination, we give them the comfort of being in control of the procedure and there is the unspoken understanding that, if the process becomes too frightening, they can turn it off.

We ask them to nod their heads once they know that the self that they are looking at has watched the film play all the way through. When a client nods, we know the trauma is already on its way to being deconditioned.

The third step is to ask them to imagine floating back into their memory of the incident at the point afterwards when they know they have survived the trauma and are safe. From this safe perspective, we then ask them to carry out the following interesting procedure: to imagine themselves going backwards quickly through their memory, like a video being rewound, to the moment prior to the onset of the traumatic event, when they were still safe and unaware of any danger.

For example, if the traumatic event was a car accident and the person was hospitalised after the accident, they might start imagining the event from the point where they are lying comfortably in the hospital bed and then go quickly through being put back on to the stretcher; being carried back out to the ambulance; the ambulance going backwards, reversing all the way to the site of the accident; themselves being carried from the ambulance into the car; lying in the car, perhaps unconscious, or in some pain or discomfort from the accident; themselves in the car prior to the moment of the crash impact; and, finally, to a time on the journey before they had any sense of an accident looming.

The two benefits that flow from this part of the process are, firstly, that the brain has no conditioned reaction to going backwards through a memory and, secondly, because it is done quickly, the brain has no time to attach feelings to the memory. This allows the information to be transferred up to the neocortex to be processed in the normal way.

We then ask the client to imagine that they are looking at the screen, holding the remote control in their hand, pressing the fast forward button and just watching the images contained in the memory going past very quickly on the screen from safe beginning to safe end. There may well be some emotion experienced at this point, but much less than if we had asked the client to do this directly. Having done this once and got a nod from the client indicating that the 'film' has reached its end, we simply take the person backwards and forwards through the memory a number of times until they show no physiological arousal whilst observing the memory on the screen. At this point the trauma is discharged and the information has been processed through the neocortex to become a part of functioning memory. It is common for clients to go home after such a session and sleep like a baby for the first time since the trauma. The crying will stop, the intrusive memories will stop, and clients will be able to mix with friends and not be fearful of talking about the accident. Their lives are transformed by a single session of counselling.

The fast phobia cure can be used for all forms of trauma resolution, whether caused by car accidents, rail crashes, muggings, rapes, heart attacks, traumatic operations, difficult births, witnessing extreme violence in war or experiencing terrorism – in fact, any event where people have been overwhelmed by fear and have not made a good recovery from the experience. It can also be used to help people who become stuck in grieving. A client of JG had suffered all the symptoms of PTSD for a great number of years. Just after he was married he was with his wife in their new car when she suddenly suffered a stroke and within two days was dead. He was so traumatised by the event that it stopped him going through the normal grieving processes. He left the house that they had bought exactly as it had been when she died, with all her things untouched. The new car remained, deteriorating, in the yard, as he could never bring himself to use it again. He rejected support from family, had no social life, and remained consumed by grief until this technique was applied to the memory of the sad death of his beautiful young wife, and freed him to live his life again.

A clear step-by-step description of the fast phobia process is set out in Appendix II.

## The three main advantages of the technique

### *It is safe*

No harm can come to people by using this technique, whereas, as we have seen, some other talking therapies can embed trauma deeper.

### *It is non-voyeuristic*

A person who has been raped, for example, can undergo this treatment without, if they so wish, having to talk to the counsellor about any of the intimate details of the experience. The counsellor doesn't watch the 'film'; the client does. A vivacious young woman came to see IT because she was having panic attacks, flashbacks, intrusive thoughts and exhibiting many other distressing symptoms of PTSD (see Appendix I). She had been attacked and raped twice, a month apart, by two different men. Both men were caught and convicted. But it meant she was living a life of high anxiety, particularly when she was in the presence of men who were attracted to her. She had changed jobs several times because of this. Because of her psychological state she had also seen a clinical psychologist and a counsellor – both of which encounters she had found disturbing, painful and useless. She hated talking about exactly what had happened. Without knowing any more detail about the rapes than you have just read she was detraumatised in one session by using the fast phobia technique. When she returned a week later she confirmed that the anxiety had gone. She reported that she had gone straight home after the session, emptied her filing cabinet of all the papers relating to the court case and thrown the papers in the dustbin "with no emotion at all". Previously, just opening the cabinet used to make her burst into tears.

***It is fast***

A person traumatised by being in a rail crash, for example, who as a consequence won't use any form of public transport, and doesn't even want to leave home, can immediately use buses and trains again after undergoing this process. This was the experience of a survivor of the Paddington rail crash who was treated by a colleague of ours at the request of the Metropolitan Police.

However, it would be quite wrong to say that treatment is always exceptionally quick. When traumas have been endured over a long period of time, although it may be possible to resolve them in a single session, some people will need long-term counselling. This is determined by how much damage was sustained to the personality while the traumatic events were ongoing. Two contrasting case histories illustrate this important point.

A young girl in her middle teens was brought to see JG suffering from acute anxiety due to her having been sexually abused over a number of years by a paedophile lodging in the family home. When she grew older, the perpetrator moved on into another family home in search of younger prey. Only then did the girl tell her mother what had been going on. The mother told the police and the police arrested the paedophile, who confessed to his crimes and is now serving a long prison sentence.

The mother then sent her daughter for 'conventional' counselling where she was encouraged to recall, in great detail, all the episodes of abuse to "get her anger out". Whilst she was in counselling her parents noticed that the young girl was becoming more and more neurotic. So they arranged for her to change to another counsellor. But the next counsellor's approach was much the same as the first and, over the next six months, the girl became progressively more neurotic and dysfunctional. At this point she was brought to see JG.

When the girl arrived it was immediately obvious that she didn't actually want to be treated by JG because she felt that this would somehow be disloyal to her current counsellor who she thought was her "best friend in the whole world". (It is interesting, as research has shown,[37] that a person can be damaged by the counselling process and yet feel that the counselling has been positively helpful. The reason for this response is that certain important emotional needs, such as the need for attention or friendship, may often be met within the counselling relationship. But the problem for which the client needs help is simultaneously being exacerbated because the counsellor doesn't know about effective treatments for trauma or depression and works in ways which make these conditions worse.)

JG explained to this young woman that, for his treatment for trauma, she did not have to give him *any* details whatsoever about the abuse. (As mentioned above, the fast phobia technique is a non-voyeuristic process.) She smiled at once, highly relieved, and she visibly relaxed. All she was asked was to give different code words for her worst memories of the abuse.

She explained that she had been abused in almost every room in the house and that, consequently, she was terrified to be in any room other than her parents' bedroom, where she currently slept because that was the only room in which she had not been abused. She gave a code word, such as 'hairbrush', for her worst memory of abuse in her own bedroom, another code word for her worst memory of abuse in her brother's bedroom, and so on for each room in the house. Then, in a single session, they detraumatised key traumatic memories relevant to each room in the house. The young lady went home tired, calm and changed.

When she came back a week later, her mother said that the girl's life had been transformed. She was now sleeping in her own bedroom for the first time since prior to the start of all her counselling. Her parents had placed their house on the market, thinking the daughter could never be happy there again, but she had now told them that she was perfectly comfortable about staying there and that they could take the house off the market. The parents themselves were now also getting along better with each other because all the trauma and stress had put them at loggerheads. So the entire family had benefited from that single first session of counselling.

This is an example of a severe degree of trauma, a substantial neurotic reaction, being able to be dealt with quickly. It was possible because the young girl's life was functional outside of the trauma itself. She had a good relationship with her parents, she was doing well in school, and her life had otherwise developed normally, so the trauma was something self-contained which could be resolved quickly.

In other cases which we might encounter, long-term work is necessary. For example, on another occasion JG saw a 21 year old man who had suffered prolonged abuse from his paedophiliac, sadistic father who had sexually tortured and raped all of his children from a very young age on a regular basis. (He is currently serving a prison sentence.) This young man had come from a totally abnormal background and had spent long periods in a zombie-like state. His unnatural upbringing meant that he had not developed normally. The inner templates – human givens – which need appropriate stimuli from the environment to complete themselves were never given the opportunity for fulfilment. He had had no experience of caring parents, loving intimacy, and so on. So, naturally, his reaction patterns were abnormal – severely neurotic or underdeveloped.

In his case, it required four years of counselling before his reaction patterns were fully retrained, enabling him to relax and have normal relationships with people, engage with the opposite sex without experiencing undue difficulties, find a meaningful job and become an independent, fully functioning, human being. For the first several months of counselling, several dozen traumatic memories were detraumatised, using the fast phobia technique but, because there were multiple dysfunctions due to his awful history, it was not a complete therapy in and of itself. In cases like that of this young man, a tremendous amount of retraining has to be done to compensate for the unfulfilled patterns which should have been unfolded, and skills which should have been acquired, during childhood and adolescence. The fast phobia technique was an essential part of the therapy, but so was the restructuring and training that took place alongside and after it.

## Curing phobias

Phobias are extremely common (see Appendix IV for the criteria). Approximately 11 per cent of the American population experience a specific phobia at some time in their life.[38] There is a marked gender difference with a lifetime prevalence among women of 15.7 per cent and 6.7 per cent for men.[39] Our, admittedly anecdotal, experience leads us to think that even more people report some degree of phobic response to certain stimuli – the most common of which are spiders, snakes, worms, flying, fear of enclosed spaces, fear of open spaces, fear of crowds and fear of heights. Indeed, as might be expected from what we have explained so far, people can develop a phobic response to *any* situation which has a similarity to situations in which they have previously experienced acute anxiety. People can be phobic of windows if they witnessed something dreadful through a window, of birds if they were ever suddenly frightened by a bird, of grass if they had a panic attack whilst standing on grass, of a particular food if they once almost choked to death whilst eating it, and so on.

The physiology of phobias is much the same as that of post traumatic stress disorder – a pattern (memory template) is imprinted in the amygdala and is trapped there, instead of being transferred to the neocortex. The template may be embedded as the result of a trauma – for example, one woman developed a cat phobia as a child after having kittens thrown at her by other children who thought it hilarious fun when the kittens' claws came out and dug into her chest. But in many cases children simply learn their phobias from their parents, because children are programmed by nature to learn the fear reactions of their primary carers. If a fearful mother hides in panic under the kitchen table every time there is lightning and a clap of thunder in the neighbourhood, it is not surprising if her children develop a phobia about thunderstorms.

However, when treating a phobia with the technique we are recommending in this monograph, we don't need to know whether a phobia was caused by a traumatic learning experience or whether it was caused by modelling. This is because the client's only need is to learn how not to be phobic in the presence of that stimulus. All that is important is the deconditioning of the response pattern. It really doesn't matter how the pattern got there.

To decondition the response pattern, we need the client to provide perhaps three or four examples – their most vivid memories – of when they felt fearful in the presence of the phobic stimulus. So, in the case of a phobia of cats, for example, the client is asked to recall three occasions when she felt very scared – a high degree of panic – in the presence of cats. For example: when, as a child, she visited her grandmother whose cat suddenly jumped up onto a garden fence in front of her; when a cat rubbed itself against her legs and when a cat unexpectedly wandered into her office at work. On all of these three occasions she would have felt extremely and unreasonably scared, with a strong urge to get away from the cat as fast as possible. So we would simply decondition each of those memories after relaxing her and using the fast phobia treatment as described. This is sufficient to detraumatise the response pattern completely.

We then encourage her to imagine, whilst still in the relaxed state, travelling into the future and seeing herself coexisting with the previously phobic stimuli in a normal manner: stroking cats, feeding them, picking them up, etc.

Often, at first, a client doesn't know for sure whether or not their phobic response has gone, so they might still retain a moderate degree of apprehension about their next encounter with the phobic object. To attenuate this reaction and this fear we try, if possible, to procure an example of the feared stimulus while clients are still with us so that they can test out their reactions for certain. So, with a cat, one would arrange for a cat to be brought into the room after the technique had been carried out. For an arachnophobic, a spider would, if possible, be caught in a glass jar and be slowly brought towards the client, but with the client always allowed to feel able to say, "Stop". As the client becomes more and more comfortable with the spider getting closer, we would suggest that, within a few minutes, the client will be able to hold the jar containing the spider, look at it closely, then take the jar outside and let the spider free.

Similarly, if someone has a phobia of lifts, we would take the client to any nearby building that has a lift and go into it with them. After accompanying the client the first time, we would then let them go up and down on their own to prove to themselves that the phobia has been deconditioned. It is, of course, only after the client has encountered the spider or gone up and down in the lift that they know that their old reaction pattern has really gone.

The client finds this process exhilarating, not only because they are freed from the inconvenience of their symptoms, but because their brain, thereafter, literally has more spare capacity once it is not using valuable energy to maintain the phobic template.

## Panic attacks and agoraphobia

Therapists working from the human givens perspective use this technique, not only for PTSD or phobias, but in other ways.

Fear of panic attacks is common among people who have experienced one – an understandable reaction since a panic attack is literally a 'dreadful' experience. This fear can easily develop into agoraphobia, where the person is so anxious and afraid of having a panic attack that they won't even leave home.

A panic attack occurs when the fight or flight reflex, the emergency reaction in the human body which prepares it to deal with physical danger, is inappropriately set off. Since people are rarely in the presence of life-threatening events, and yet still suffer from panic attacks, it is clear that they are mostly triggered off by a progressive rising in an individual's background stress levels. There comes a point when one more stress – and it can be quite a small one – becomes the straw that breaks the camel's back. Panic is the result. The person doesn't understand why their heart is pounding, why they are sweating, why their breathing rate is accelerating – all natural reactions to stress – and so jumps to the conclusion that something is seriously wrong (typically that they are having a heart attack), which causes even more alarm and more adrenaline to be released, magnifying the symptoms further.

During this extreme alarm arousal the brain, naturally enough, is scanning the environment to find out what the source of this alarm could be, noting all kinds of accompanying details and storing them in the amygdala for future reference. Not surprisingly then, for many people, the association is with the environment where the panic attack happened. If it happened in a supermarket, in future the person will tend to avoid supermarkets. But because the panic attack was not caused by the supermarket but by raised stress levels, the next time the person feels over stressed, perhaps in a post office queue, they may experience another panic attack and so start avoiding post offices as well – and so on. Progressively the noose of agoraphobia develops, forming a stranglehold that restricts the person's ability to continue with any normal life.

A combination of relaxation, behaviour and cognitive therapy is a useful treatment modality for this condition: in other words, teaching the person to deal with whatever is raising their stress levels, calm themselves down and progressively re-engage with life. However, this process is rapidly accelerated if the memories of their most frightening panic attacks are detraumatised first. Then the brain won't be pattern matching from the previous panic attack to whatever situation they are going into next. This greatly helps the recovery process.

It's much easier to work with panic attack cases once one understands that the memory templates of past panic attacks have became locked into the emotional brain. Then it is possible to go ahead and do what is necessary to turn them into ordinary memories.

We would say it is essential, for people who have developed agoraphobia, that the pattern matches to environments that disturb them – typically, supermarkets, high streets, schools, tube trains, or any potentially crowded public situation – are defused in this way. They then need help to rehearse imaginatively, in their relaxed REM trance state, entering those environments in a calm manner and going about their business normally. This rehearsal, by giving them a new mental template to match to, helps them more readily re-enter these situations in reality. Usual practice is to establish and agree with the client a hierachical scale of feared situations and work through them, from least to most feared.

## Obsessive compulsive disorder (OCD)

Obsessions are thoughts, images or impulses that cause marked degrees of anxiety or distress. Compulsions are repetitively carried out behaviours (such as hand washing) or thoughts (such as silently repeating prayers) that follow rigid rules and are performed in an attempt to reduce the distress brought on by the obsessions or as a way of making reparation for intrusive scary thoughts.

But OCD is a very unforgiving god, because the more rituals carried out to appease it, the more the frightening thoughts recur. As with agoraphobia, the noose gets pulled tighter and tighter and the person's area of effective functioning shrinks ever smaller. Every time sufferers carry out a ritual, they reinforce the OCD; just as every time an agoraphobic avoids going out they reinforce their particular fear pattern.

Two to three people in every hundred suffer from OCD.[40] We find that OCD responds well to the fast phobia technique during which the fear of *not* performing the obsessive behaviour is detraumatised (thus making it less frightening), followed by getting the sufferer to rehearse in a dissociated state what it will be like to live *without* doing the abnormal behaviour or having the compulsive thoughts.

As with panic attacks, the triggering factor in OCD seems to be raised stress levels which may be due to anything from physical illness to a fright, lack of sleep, business worries, relationship breakdown or exam worries. Some people have a propensity to develop this disorder in response to raised stress levels.

Clients are clearly terrified of cutting out their rituals, whether they are washing their hands 50 times in case their son will be killed in an accident in school, or whether they are stacking all their clothes up in a particular order in their bedroom because otherwise they think they will get a terrible disease. The strong emotion aroused locks them into a trance state. (OCD sufferers usually have no sense of time whilst carrying out their rituals, nor often can they remember whether they have done the ritual properly or not, resulting in the perceived need to perform it over and over. Such time distortion and amnesia are both hypnotic phenomena.)

In their trance the intrusive thought, like a powerful post hypnotic suggestion, instructs the individual that they must perform the behaviour to relieve the fear. This is clearly not rational thinking but just as when, in the REM state, we dream and believe in the reality of the dream, so do the entranced OCD sufferers believe in the reality of the OCD ritual and its consequences. They have no alternative, just as we cannot easily avoid dreaming. The thought of stopping the rituals genuinely frightens them.

One of the key steps in working with OCD – as in effective therapy for any symptomatology – is for the therapist to help the client to separate their core identity from their problem. In this process, by whatever means, the therapist or counsellor helps the sufferer to take a step back into their observing self and recognise that the OCD is not part of who they are. It is outside them, separate but impinging in unwelcome ways.

Once the person can see themselves as separate from OCD they can recognise and separate out an OCD thought from a normal thought. This is vital: developing the ability to recognise when the OCD is in charge as distinct from when their brain is functioning normally.

Essentially we want to keep the person in their observing self so that they can observe the OCD and keep their distance from it. Whenever they recognise the OCD thoughts intruding, they must have some form of distraction instantly available to them to pull their attention away from the OCD thought and calm them down.

A useful tactic is to replace the problematic behavioural rituals with less problematic ones and for people to have these harmless rituals prepared in advance so that they can switch into them when they need to distract themselves from the OCD thoughts. The harmless rituals can be anything such as aerobic activity, listening to music, calling a friend on the phone, reading a book of poetry or watching a drama on television – anything that they can immediately engage with as a means of distraction so as to avoid carrying out the rituals that the OCD is commanding them to perform.

As the client learns to avoid, or minimise, carrying out the rituals, a feedback mechanism is set up from the environment, saying, in effect, to the primitive part of the brain affected by the OCD, "Look, these thoughts aren't real ... those imagined bad consequences aren't happening". Once enough of this feedback is received, the OCD thoughts are switched off.

This is where the fast phobia technique can be so useful with OCD. We get the client, in a calm, relaxed and dissociated state, to see themselves on a TV screen, experiencing the frightening thought, but not carrying out the rituals. For instance, they experience, in a dissociated state, the OCD thought instructing them to wash their hands repeatedly, otherwise their son will die, and then watch themselves *not* washing their hands but, instead, doing something entirely different, such as knitting or doing a crossword, with no adverse consequences. Once they have that novel idea in their mind, associated with a relaxed state, they have created a new template that says, in effect, "I don't have to carry out the rituals".

Here is a case history that illustrates how OCD can be reduced in this way. A man worked in a garage in charge of the spare parts division. His father, at the age of 40, had died of a heart attack. When he himself reached the age of 40 he had a panic attack and made the common assumption that it was a heart attack. He went along to his GP who checked him out and told him his heart was absolutely fine. But the raised stress levels triggered off OCD in him. He started to get scary thoughts and developed rituals to appease the thoughts.

Two primary rituals caused him maximum distress. The first was that, every day on his way home from work at the garage, the thought would occur to him that he had knocked somebody down, even though he had no awareness of doing so. He imagined someone lying unconscious on the road, bleeding to death as a result of his careless driving. This thought would become so powerful that, by the time he got home, he was in acute anxiety and would have to drive slowly back all the 30 miles to the garage to check that there had been no accident. This ritual took up a large portion of each evening.

The second ritual causing him distress was that, when customers were leaving the garage after work had been done on their cars, the thought would occur to him that he might have supplied the wrong parts to be fitted. He would visualise the car catching fire and burning the occupants to death. He would experience extreme anxiety, rush out to retrieve the car from the customer and check the new part against the stock just to make sure it was the right one. This, of course, distressed customers and the management of the garage alike.

One useful aspect of working with people with OCD is that, if we give them something to do, they can become quite obsessive about carrying out our instructions, so we can use this compulsive tendency productively to facilitate the treatment. The first intervention with this man was to use guided imagery to help him achieve a deep state of relaxation. JG got him to imagine himself somewhere really peaceful and safe – the first step in the fast phobia cure. This was recorded on tape and included the message loud and clear: "Isn't it nice to know that your doctor has thoroughly checked you over and you have a sound, strong, healthy heart?" because that was the worry that had triggered off the OCD in the first place. During that first session JG also gave the client the instruction that each evening, as soon as he got home, he was to rush into his house, go to his bedroom and sit down and listen to this relaxation tape, rather than drive back to the garage. He reinforced this by encouraging the man to visualise himself, via the fast phobia technique, coming home from work and listening to his tape, with no adverse consequences.

The man did this for a couple of weeks and, as he found that there were no unidentified bodies being discovered on the road between his house and the garage, no hit-and-run stories appearing in the local newspapers, the feedback message from reality got into his brain and the obsessive thought faded away. He was then ready to deal with his next great fear which centred around handing out spare car parts at the garage.

He was excellent at his job. He knew by heart every spare part the garage had in stock, but this problem of fearing he had supplied the wrong part was overwhelming him. One important counselling principle is that, if a problem is too big to solve in one go, the best thing is to break it down into smaller chunks and deal with each one.

This is the approach that JG took. When the thought occurred to the man that the wrong part had been fitted to a car, instead of rushing out and retrieving it to make sure it was the right part – to not check would have left him in such an acute state of anxiety that he would be dysfunctional for the rest of the day – he agreed to alter the ritual. In future, on handing out a spare part, he would write the number of the part in a notebook. Then, after the customer had left with the car, when he felt the anxiety about having given out the wrong part rising, he would go to the stockroom and check the number in his notebook against the stock to make sure the right part had been used. Doing this no longer disrupted the smooth running of the garage and started to moderate his anxiety, making it more tolerable. Again, after a few weeks, the obsessive thought just died away.

JG saw him on a weekly basis for about six weeks, using the fast phobia technique on each occasion and showing him how to focus his attention outwards and think more positively and constructively, till the OCD was completely eliminated. Well, in truth, there was still one ritual left. He was still listening to the tape compulsively! So, the final step in the therapeutic procedure was to wean him off that.

In this case history we can see at work several principles of effective therapy which always work from the human givens: relaxation, enabling the person to go into their observing self; separation of the observing self from the problem; the principle of dissociation in order to facilitate a more realistic template being introduced to the amygdala and to accelerate the development of desired behaviour patterns; the use of imagination; drawing on clients' own resources; chunking problems so that they can be solved, etc.

Social phobia, fear of job interviews and exams can be helped in much the same way.

## The chair's problem

Milton H. Erickson, the American psychiatrist and renowned hypnotherapist who inspired the development of the techniques we have described, used a method to cure phobias that was even shorter than the one which we have outlined. He found that it worked with good hypnotic subjects, although he seems not to have recognised that the phobic or traumatised state is *always* associated with good hypnotic subjects – such disorders are their vulnerability.

Once he had a phobic person sitting in a deeply relaxed trance in a comfortable chair he would ask them to recall, what it felt like to be very frightened of whatever their phobia concerned. At the point when they were aroused to a high state of anxiety and very uncomfortable with that anxious feeling, he would ask them if they would like to lose their anxiety. When they nodded their head, he would say something like, "In a moment ... I'm going to ask you to stand up and move to this chair over here ... and to leave your fear behind you in that chair". Because the subject was in a deeply hypnotic state – the REM state, which is the programming part of the mind – the phobic's brain was receptive enough to take on board that instruction. They would move chairs and lose their phobia.[41]

We now know that what Erickson was doing was taking the fear template in the amygdala, the pattern of feeling fear of flying or of cats or of thunder or whatever, and confining its reaction pattern to one stimulus only, namely the chair with which the brain now associates it. Indeed, when subjects came out of trance, Erickson would later ask them to sit down on the first chair again and their strong feeling of fear would instantly return because their amygdala would pattern match to the original template now associated with that specific chair in his office.

Erickson's rapid technique is as effective a cure as going through the fast phobia process we've described here. The difficulty, though, is that one does need great confidence in using hypnotic skills and a deeply hypnotic state in the client in order to effect the restriction of a phobic response pattern to a specific chair. However, his technique neatly illustrates the mechanics by which post traumatic stress disorder and phobias are developed – a pattern in the amygdala is seeking its counterpart in the environment, seeking something to match up to.

For the sufferer from PTSD, phobic responses, panic or OCD, it doesn't matter how the result is achieved. Whether we remove this pattern from the amygdala with the fast phobia cure and get it processed through the neocortex as an ordinary memory, or change it by restricting the application of the pattern to an innocuous stimulus, as Erickson showed could be done, either way the distressing symptom is reliably disabled and dealt with, and the misery gone.

* * * * *

# APPENDIX I

## Criteria for Post Traumatic Stress Disorder

**A** The person has been exposed to a traumatic event in which both of the following were present:

1) the person experienced, witnessed, or was confronted with an event or events that involved actual or threatened death or serious injury or a threat to the physical integrity of self or others
2) the person's responses involved intense fear, helplessness, or horror.

**B** The traumatic event is persistently re-experienced in one (or more) of the following ways:

1) recurrent and intrusive distressing recollections of the event, including images, thoughts, or perceptions
2) recurrent distressing dreams connected to the event
3) acting or feeling as if the traumatic event were recurring (includes a sense of reliving the experience, illusions, hallucinations, and dissociative flashback episodes, including those that occur on awakening or when intoxicated)
4) intense psychological distress at exposure to internal or external cues that symbolise or resemble an aspect of the traumatic event
5) physiological reactivity on exposure to internal or external cues that symbolise or resemble an aspect of the traumatic event.

**C** Persistent avoidance of stimuli associated with the trauma and numbing of general responsiveness (not present before the trauma) as indicated by three (or more) of the following:

1) efforts to avoid thoughts, feelings, or conversations associated with the trauma
2) efforts to avoid activities, places, or people that arouse recollections of the trauma
3) inability to recall an important aspect of the trauma

4) marked diminished interest or participation in significant activities
5) feeling of detachment or estrangement from others
6) restricted range of affect (eg. unable to have loving feelings)
7) sense of a foreshortened future (eg. does not expect to have a career, marriage, children, or a normal life span).

**D** Persistent symptoms of increased arousal (not present before the trauma), as indicated by two (or more) of the following:

1) difficulty falling or staying asleep
2) irritability or outbursts of anger
3) difficulty in concentrating
4) hyper-vigilance
5) exaggerated startle response.

**E** Duration of the disturbance (symptoms in Criteria B, C, and D) is more than one month.

**F** The disturbance causes clinically significant distress or impairment in social, occupational or other important areas of functioning.

# APPENDIX II

## Fast Phobia Cure

### *The stages of the process*

The following steps should be done initially with guidance from an experienced practitioner. We recommend attendance at a workshop where you can witness PTSD and/or phobias being cured and practise each stage. (Phone MindFields on 01323 811440 for details of training availability.)

1. Relax the patient and ask them to remember a time or a place when they felt totally safe and at ease – perhaps on a beach, lazing in a garden, in their bedroom – wherever they choose. Build on this until they are in a receptive trance state.
2. Ask the patient to imagine that, in that 'special' peaceful place, they have a TV set and a video player with a remote control facility that they can control.
3. Get them to float to one side of themselves, out of their body, and look at themselves watching the screen without actually seeing the picture. This can seem dream-like, like an 'out of body' experience. (In trance, people accept this very easily – just as they would in a dream.) Then ask them to watch themselves watching a film of themselves that begins *before* the traumatic event. (After each stage throughout the process, get them to signal to you that they have completed it. A nod of the head will do. You can also explain that *"the unconscious can do this quickly".*) Start the experience before the incident, then run right through till after the incident is over and they feel safe again in a quiet scene or a single, peaceful, still frame of the 'film'.
4. If, during the process, you sense them tensing, becoming afraid, bring them back to their peaceful place by speaking in a calm reassuring way. When they have calmed down you simply carry on with the process.

5. Have the patient float back into themselves and experience the memory of the traumatic event going quickly *backwards* – like rewinding a video.
6. Then ask them to be in front of the screen and, by pressing the fast forward button on the remote control, watch the images going by very quickly from beginning to end.
7. Repeat steps 5 and 6 until the scenes evoke no emotion, even if it takes six or seven goes. Make sure that the client has plenty of time to accomplish this.
8. If we want the client to develop competence in handling a situation in future, for example if the trauma was a car crash and they want to be able to be at ease travelling in cars again, or if they had a phobia develop as the result of being attacked by a dog and they want to respond to dogs as they did before being attacked, get them to rehearse in their imagination feeling calm, relaxed and confident in such a situation.
9. Then bring them out of trance and let them reorientate to the room. If appropriate, you can help the client there and then experience themselves not reacting in a fearful way in reality to a phobic stimulus.

# APPENDIX III

## Eye-movement desensitization and reprocessing (EMDR)[42]

This is a technique that has been applied to treating PTSD and there is considerable anecdotal evidence for its usefulness. It was developed by Francine Shapiro, an American psychologist, and involves getting clients to recall traumatic episodes whilst their eyes track the movement of the therapist's hand back and forth in front of them. Several episodes of the eye tracking the hand movements may be required for a particular traumatic sequence to diminish in its emotional intensity. (Many EMDR practitioners now use a moving light to automate the process.)

Shapiro admits that she doesn't know why the technique appears to work, although she thinks there may be a connection with the rapid eye movement of REM sleep.

In the light of the organising idea presented in this monograph it is not difficult to see how it could be that this technique could sometimes work. The trauma is encoded by the amygdala and every time the client suffering from PTSD tries to recall it, they go so fully back into the memory, into the trance state of the trauma, that they relive the trauma as if it were happening *now.* Any process that cures PTSD has to keep the person's awareness focused in the present so that their higher cortex can reframe the memory as a *past* event and in a realistic perspective.[43]

The rapid eye movements induced by following the therapist's moving hand (an ancient hypnotic technique – remember the old films of hypnotists swinging their pocket watches and repeating ... "sleep ... sleep") keeps the patient's attention focused on the present whilst allowing part of their attention to be engaged by the trauma. In other words the patient is encouraged to view the trauma in a disassociated state which lowers the emotional arousal. The neocortex is then activated and the observing self is able to recode and reframe the event as in the past and of only limited relevance and significance in the present. This somewhat crude and mechanical procedure may for these reasons be effective in treating some cases of trauma.

# APPENDIX IV

## Criteria for specific phobia

**A** There is marked and persistent fear that is excessive or unreasonable, cued by the presence or anticipation of a specific object or situation (eg. flying, heights, animals, receiving an injection, seeing blood).

**B** Exposure to the phobic stimulus almost invariably provokes an immediate anxiety response, which may take the form of a situationally bound or situationally predisposed panic attack. *Note:* In children, the anxiety may be expressed by crying, tantrums, freezing or clinging.

**C** The person recognises that the fear is excessive or unreasonable. *Note:* In children this feature may be absent.

**D** The phobic situation(s) is avoided or else is endured with intense anxiety or distress.

**E** The avoidance, anxious anticipation, or distress in the feared situation(s) interferes significantly with the person's normal routine, occupational (or academic) functioning, or social activities or relationships, or there is marked distress about having the phobia.

**F** In individuals under the age of 18 years, the duration is at least 6 months.

Specific phobias would include:

**Animal type**

**Natural environment type** (eg. heights, storms, water)

**Blood – injections – injury type**

**Situational type** (eg. aeroplanes, lifts, enclosed places)

**Other type** (eg. phobic avoidance of situations that may lead to choking, vomiting, or contracting an illness; in children, avoidance of loud sounds, balloons or costumed characters).

## APPENDIX V

The observing self is a human given. Arthur Deikman, the American psychiatrist who coined the term, described it as: "the transparent centre, that which is aware. It is the most personal self of all because it supersedes thought, feeling, and action, for it experiences these functions. No matter what takes place, no matter what we experience, nothing is as central as the self that observes. In the face of this phenomenon, Descartes' starting point, 'I think; therefore, I am,' must yield to the more basic position, 'I am aware; therefore, I am.'

"The most important fact about the observing self is that it is incapable of being objectified. When you try to locate it to establish its boundaries, the task is impossible; whatever you can notice or conceptualize is already an object of awareness, not awareness itself, which seems to jump a step back when we experience an object. Unlike every other aspect of experience – thoughts, emotions, desires, and functions – the observing self can be known but not located, not 'seen'.

"There is a Yogic discipline that prescribes the exercise of 'Who am I?' to demonstrate that the observing self is not an object; it does not belong to the domains of thinking, feeling, or action: 'If I lost my arm, I would still exist, therefore, I am not my arm. If I could not hear, I would still exist. Therefore, I am not my hearing.' And so on, until finally, 'I am not this thought,' which leads to a radically different experience of the self.

"Western psychotherapy has yet to confront this paradox. The infinite regression of awareness, like two mirrors placed face to face, has largely been a subject for philosophers rather than scientists. The psychiatric and psychological literature refers to the observing self as 'the observing ego', but does not explore the special nature of that 'ego' and its implications for our understanding of the self.

"The observing self is not part of the object world formed by our thoughts and sensory perception because, literally, it has no limits; everything else does. Thus, everyday consciousness contains a transcendent element that we seldom notice because that element is the very ground of our experience. The word transcendent is justified because if subjective consciousness – the observing self – cannot itself be observed but remains forever apart from the contents of consciousness, it is likely to be of a different order from everything else. Its fundamentally different nature becomes evident when we realize that the observing self is featureless; it cannot be affected by the world any more than a mirror can be affected by the images it reflects.

"In the midst of the finite world is the 'I', and it doesn't belong in that world. It is obviously different from the world but the difference is ignored. All else can be objectified, has limits and boundaries that can be described. All else is a segment of the world of fixed or relative dimensions. The observing self, however, is not like anything else we know."

(Appendix V was adapted from material found in *The Observing Self* by Dr Arthur Deikman.)

## References

1. Charney, D. S., Deutch, A.V., Krystal, J. H., Southwick, A. M., and Davis, M. (1993) Psychobiologic mechanisms of post-traumatic stress disorder. *Archives of General Psychiatry,* 50, 295–305.
2. Kessler, R. C., Sonnega, A., Bromet, E., Hughes, M., and Nelson, C.B., (1995) Post traumatic stress disorder in the National Comorbidity Survey. *Archives of General Psychiatry*, 52, 1048–1060.
3. Danieli, Y. (1985) The treatment and prevention of long-term effects and intergenerational transmission of victimization. A lesson from Holocaust survivors and their children. In C. R. Figley (ed.). *Trauma and its Wake* (pp. 278–294) Bruner/Mazel.
4. Nathan P. E., Gorman, J. M., eds. (1998) *A Guide to Treatments that Work.* Oxford University Press.
5. Wessely, S., Rose, S., Bisson, J. A. (1999) A systematic review of brief psychological interventions ("debriefing") for the treatment of immediate trauma related symptoms and the prevention of post traumatic stress disorder. In Cochrane Collaboration. *Cochrane Library*, Issue 4, Oxford.
6. Debunking debriefing. *The New Therapist,* 7, 1, 8.
7. Spiegel, D., Hunt, T., and Dondershine, H. E. (1988) Dissociation and hypnotisability in post traumatic stress disorder. *American Journal of Psychiatry*, 145, 301–305
8. Tehrani, N. (1998) Debriefing: a safe way to defuse emotion? *The Therapist,* 5, 3. "If a trauma victim is debriefed in a state of high emotion, the process can increase the arousal to the point of overload, trapping the sensory impressions in the amygdala."
9. Griffin, J. and Tyrrell, I. (1999) *Psychotherapy and the Human Givens.* European Therapy Studies Institute.
10. Griffin, J. and Tyrrell, I. (2000) *The APET model: Patterns in the brain.* HG Publishing.
11. Jouvet, M. (1978) Does a genetic programming of the brain occur during paradoxical sleep? P. A. Buser & A. Rougel-Buser (eds.) *Cerebral Correlates of Conscious Experience,* Elsevier.
12. Griffin, J. (1997) *The Origin of Dreams.* The Therapist Ltd.
13. Gopnik, A., Meltzoff, A. and Kuhl, P. (1999) *How Babies Think.* Weidenfeld & Nicolson.
14. Hoffman, D. D., (1998) *Visual Intelligence: how we create what we see.* W. W. Norton & Company.
15. LeDoux, J. E. (1992) Emotion as memory: anatomical systems underlying indelible neural traces. In S. A. Christensen (ed.) *Handbook of Emotion and Memory*. Erlbaum, Hillsdale New Jersey.
16. Wilson, J. P., and Keane, T. M. (1997) *Assessing Psychological Trauma and PTSD.* The Guildford Press.

17. ibid.

18. Van der Kolk (1996) In B. A. Van der Kolk, McFarlane and Weisaeth (eds.) *Traumatic Stress*. Guildford Press.

19. Kardiner, A. (1941) *The Traumatic Neuroses of War.* New York.

20. Goleman, D. (1996) *Emotional Intelligence*. Bloomsbury, London.

21. Dixon, A. K. (1998) Ethological strategies for defence in animals and humans: their role in some psychiatric disorders. *British Journal of Medical Psychology*, 71, 417–445.

22. Blanchard, R. J., and Blanchard, D. C. (1989) Antipredator defensive behaviour. *Journal of Comparative Psychology*, 103, 70–82. "If something unexpected occurs – a loud noise or sudden movement – people tend to respond immediately ... stop what they are doing ... orient toward the stimulus, and try to identify its potentiality for actual danger. This happens very quickly, in a reflex-like sequence in which action precedes any voluntary or consciously intentioned behaviour. A poorly localisable or identifiable threat source, such as a sound in the night, may elicit an active immobility so profound that the frightened person can hardly speak or even breathe, i.e. freezing. However, if the danger source has been localised and an avenue for flight or concealment is plausible, the person will probably try to flee or hide."

23. Levine, P. (1998) *Waking the Tiger.* North Atlantic Books.

24. Levine, P. (1998) Blowing off stress. *The Therapist,* 5, 2.

25. Morrison, A. R. & Reiner, P. B. (1985) A dissection of paradoxical sleep. In D. J. McGinty, C. Drucken, A. R. Morrison and P. Parmeggiani (eds.), *Brain Mechanisms of Sleep.* Raven Press, New York, 97–110.

26. Griffin, J. (1997) *The Origin of Dreams.* The Therapist Ltd.

27. Griffin, J. and Tyrrell, I. (1998) *Hypnosis and Trance States: a new psychobiological explanation.* European Therapy Studies Institute.

28. Spiegel, D., Detrick, D. and Frischholz, E. J. (1982) Hypnotizability and psychopathology. *American Journal of Psychiatry,* 139, 431–437.

29. Shephard, B. (2000) *A War of Nerves: soldiers and psychiatrists 1914–1994.* Jonathan Cape.

30. ibid.

31. Brown. W. (1934) *Psychology and Psychotherapy.* London.

32. Sargant, W. (1957) *Battle for the Mind.* Heinemann.

33. Deikman, A. J. (1982). *The Observing Self.* Beacon Press.

34. ibid.

35. Amaral, D. G., Price, J. L., Pitkanen, A. and Carmichael S. T. (1992). Anatomical organization of the primate amygdaloid complex. In J. P. Aggleton (ed.) *The amygdala: neurobiological aspects of emotion, memory and mental dysfunction.* Wiley-Liss, New York (pp 1–66).

36. The MindFields College prospectus can be obtained by telephoning 01323 811440 in the UK. Their website is www.mindfields.org.uk

37. Harrison & Harrison (1998) Unproven assumptions about the impact of bereavement on children. *Journal of the Royal Society of Medicine.* Volume 92, May 98.

38. Kessler, R. C., McGonagle, K. A., Zhao, S. et al. (1994) Lifetime and 12-month prevalence of DSM-III-psychiatric disorders in the United States: results from the National Comorbidity Survey. *Archives of General Psychiatry*, 16, 118–126.

39. Anthony, M. M., and Barlow, D. H. (1996) Specific phobia. In V. E. Caballo & R. M. Turner (eds.), *International Handbook of Cognitive/Behavioural Treatment of Psychiatric Disorders.* Madrid, Siglio XXI.

40. Karno, M., Golding, J. M., Sorenson, S. B., & Burnham, M.A. (1988) The epidemiology of obsessive-compulsive disorder. *Archives of General Psychiatry*, 45, 12, 1094–1099.

41. O'Hanlon, W. H. (1987) *Taproots – Underlying principles of Milton Erickson's therapy and hypnosis.* W. W. Norton.

42. Shapiro, F., and Forrest, M. S. (1997) *EMDR.* Basic Books.

43. Wolinsky, S. (1991) *Trances People Live By.* The Bramble Co. Wolinsky gives a clear description of how a person slips into an age regressed hypnotic trance when they relive a trauma. He developed a technique very similar to Shapiro's, which keeps the patient's awareness focused on the therapist whilst recalling the trauma, thus blocking them from regressing completely into the traumatic memory. His technique also keeps emotional arousal from rising too high, facilitating the reframing and a recoding of the memory by the higher cortex.

## About the authors

**JOE GRIFFIN** is a psychologist with a thriving psychotherapy practice. Over the last decade thousands of health professionals have enjoyed his practical workshops and seminars on effective psychotherapy and counselling. He is widely recognised as one of the most informed and entertaining speakers on the subject having studied with many of the leading figures of the psychotherapy world. He spent 12 years researching why animals and humans evolved to dream. The resulting book which describes the breakthrough he made in this field, *The Origin of Dreams,* offered the first holistic synthesis – a recognition of the interdependence of the biological and the psychological – to explain the origin, function and meaning of dreams. His findings about mental processes have been described by scientific reviewers as, "the key to all psychic states ... an important milestone ... moves our understanding on significantly ... a watershed in our exploration of the evolution of mental processes." He is currently working on a new way of understanding evolutionary processes.

**IVAN TYRRELL** is a psychotherapist (specialising in brief therapy for depression and anxiety disorders) and a writer with a particular interest in the psychology of perception. He is a founder member of the European Therapy Studies Institute (ETSI) which, in 1992, launched *The Therapist* – the popular multi-disciplinary magazine for all caring professionals. His work for *The Therapist* (now called *Human Givens: the mental health journal*) involves him in a continuing programme of writing, interviewing, and investigating the latest developments in psychology, psychotherapy and the study of human behaviour. He lectures at educational and medical institutions throughout the UK. The *British Medical Journal* said of his book, *The Survival Option,* published by Jonathan Cape, "his practical information is reliable", and *The Times* wrote that it contained, "facts, not emotion... should be in every home in the country." Both he and Joe Griffin are members of the group involved with developing the 'human givens' approach to applying knowledge of human psychology and behaviour to psychotherapy, counselling and education.